HAIL REDEEMER
A LENTEN CANTATA
FOR CHORUS & ORGAN

Christopher Tambling

Kevin
Mayhew

We hope you enjoy the music in this book. Further copies are available
from your local music shop or Christian bookshop.

In case of difficulty, please contact the publisher direct by writing to:

The Sales Department
KEVIN MAYHEW LTD
Rattlesden
Bury St Edmunds
Suffolk
IP30 0SZ

Phone 01449 737978
Fax 01449 737834

Please ask for our complete catalogue of outstanding Church Music.

First published in Great Britain in 1996 by Kevin Mayhew Ltd.

© Copyright 1996 Kevin Mayhew Ltd.

ISBN 0 86209 907 2
Catalogue No: 1450063

0 1 2 3 4 5 6 7 8 9

Front Cover: *The Road to Calvary* by Fra Angelico (c.1387-1455).
Courtesy of Museo di San Marco dell'Angelico, Florence/Bridgeman Art Library.
Reproduced by kind permission.
Cover design by Graham Johnstone and Stephen Judd.

Music Editor: Stephanie Hill
Music setting by Sarah McCarter

Printed and bound in Great Britain by
Caligraving Limited Thetford Norfolk

Contents

PUBLISHERS' NOTE

Hail Redeemer is scored for SATB choir with soloists and organ. Optional string parts are available from the Publisher.

For Edward, on his first Communion Day, Corpus Christi 1995

HAIL! REDEEMER

Christopher Tambling (b.1964)

Congregational Hymn

1 FORTY DAYS AND FORTY NIGHTS

v1&6 All
v4 Low voices

1. For - ty days and for - ty nights thou wast fast - ing in the wild;
4. And if Sa - tan, vex - ing sore, flesh or spi - rit should as - sail,
6. Keep, O keep us, Sa - viour dear, e - ver con - stant by thy side,

verses 1&4 — *verse 6* — *Fine*

for - ty days and for - ty nights temp - ted, and yet un - de - filed.
thou, his van - quish - er be - fore, grant we may not faint nor fail.
that with thee we may ap - pear at the e - ter - nal East - er - tide.

v3 Choir only (unaccompanied)
v5 Low voices only (unison)

2. Sun - beams scorch - ing all the day, chil - ly dew - drops
3. Let us thine en - dur - ance share, and a - while from
5. So shall we have peace di - vine, ho - lier glad - ness

v5 High voices only (unison)

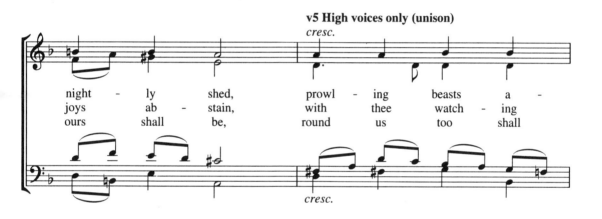

night - ly shed, prowl - ing beasts a -
joys ab - stain, with thee watch - ing
ours shall be, round us too shall

D.C. after vs. 3 & 5

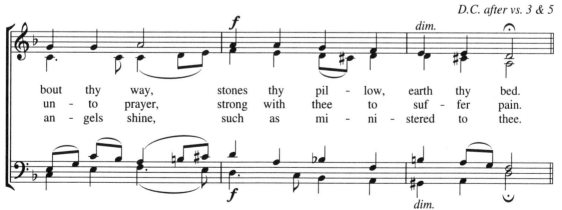

bout thy way, stones thy pil - low, earth thy bed.
un - to prayer, strong with thee to suf - fer pain.
an - gels shine, such as mi - ni - stered to thee.

Melody: 'Aus der Tiefe'; from Nürnbergisches Gesangbuch (1676)
Text: George Hunt Smyttan (1822-1870) and Francis Pott (1832-1909)

Stand.

2 THE AGONY

but there are two great spa-cious things, the which to

mea-sure it doth more be - hove; yet few there are that

sound them, sin and love.

Sopranos and Altos

Who would know sin, let him re-pair un - to Mount O - li-vet;

there let him see a man so wrung with pains, that all his hair, his
skin, his gar-ments bloo-dy be. Sin is that press and
vice, which for-ceth pain to hunt his cru-el food through ev-'ry vein.

Who knows not love, let him as - say and taste that juice which, on the

(for rehearsal only)

cross, a pike did set a - gain a - broach; then let him say if e - ver he did

but I as wine.

but I as wine.

but I as wine.

feels as blood, but I as wine.

Text: George Herbert (1593-1633)

Sir Reading

3 HIS STATE WAS DIVINE

Stand.

Slowly (♩ = 76)

mp   *cresc.*

His state was di - vine, yet Christ Je - sus did not cling to his e -

mp   *cresc.*

mf   with God,

qual - i - ty with God, his e - qual - i - ty with God   but

mf

May be sung unaccompanied

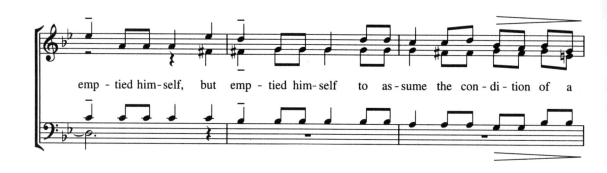

emp - tied him-self, but emp - tied him-self to as - sume the con - di - tion of a

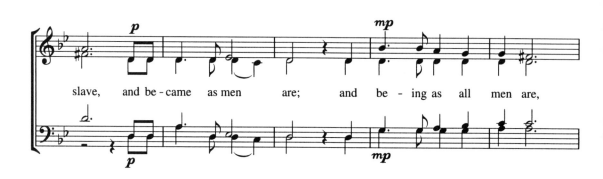

slave, and be - came as men are; and be - ing as all men are,

he was hum - bler yet, e - ven to ac - cept - ing death,

he was hum - bler yet,
cresc.

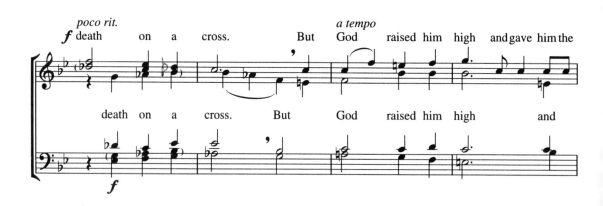

death on a cross. But God raised him high and gave him the

death on a cross. But God raised him high and

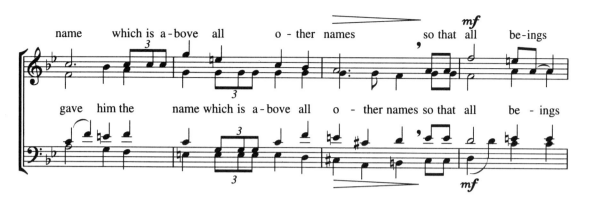

name — which is a-bove all — o-ther names — so that all — be-ings

gave — him the — name which is a-bove all — o - ther names so that all — be - ings

in the heav'ns, on — earth and in the — un - der - world should bend the knee — at the

name — of Je - sus — and that ev — ery tongue should ac-claim — Je - sus

Christ — as Lord, — to the glo — ry of God the — Fa - ther.

straight on

Text: Philippians 2:6-11

4 O SAVIOUR OF THE WORLD

O Sa-viour of the world, through your

cross and pre-cious blood you have gi-ven us new life.

Save

15

Text: *Collect for the visitation of the sick from 'Book of Common Prayer' adapted by Christopher Tambling*

5 RIDE ON, RIDE ON IN MAJESTY!

v1 Unison

1. Ride on, ride on in ma - jes - ty! Hark, all the tribes ho - san - na cry; thy hum - ble beast pur - sues his road with palms and scat - tered gar - ments strowed.

Harmony

2. Ride on, ride on in majesty!
   In lowly pomp ride on to die;
   O Christ, thy triumphs now begin
   o'er captive death and conquered sin.

High voices

3. Ride on, ride on in majesty!
   The wingèd squadrons of the sky
   look down with sad and wond'ring eyes
   to see th'approaching sacrifice.

Low voices

4. Ride on, ride on in majesty!
   Thy last and fiercest strife is nigh;
   the Father, on his sapphire throne,
   awaits his own anointed Son.

Unison

5. Ride on, ride on in majesty!
   In lowly pomp ride on to die;
   bow thy meek head to mortal pain,
   then take, O God, thy pow'r, and reign.

Melody: 'Winchester New', from Musikalisches Handbuch (1690)
Text: Henry Hart Milman (1791-1868) alt.

Sit
(Pause)

Stand.

6 MAN BORN OF A WOMAN

* *Alternatively, solo can be sung by all Sopranos.*

20

from the pains of e - ter - nal death.

mp You know the se - crets of our hearts, the
mp You know the se - crets of our hearts, the se - crets
mp You know the se - crets of our hearts; in your mer - cy hear our prayer, for -

crets of our hearts; in your mer - cy hear our prayer, for -
se - crets of our hearts; in your mer - cy hear our prayer, for -
know the se - crets of our hearts; hear our prayer, for -
of our hearts; in your mer - cy hear our prayer, for -

Back to p.19.

D.S. al Fine

fall a - way from you.

give us our sins, and at our last hour let us not fall a - way from you.

us not fall a - way from you.

D.S. al Fine

Text: The Funeral Service

7 HE ENDURED THE SUFFERING

Stay seated

Gently (♩ = 92)

He en-dured the suf - fer - ing that should have been ours, the

pain that we should have borne.

N But we are healed by the pu-nish-ment he suf - fered, made

whole by the blows he re - ceived. **O**

Stand

Stand

8 MY GOD, MY GOD,
WHY HAVE YOU FORSAKEN ME?

Text: verses from Psalm 21

9 WHEN I SURVEY THE WONDROUS CROSS

Freely (♩ = 120)
Sopranos (or Soprano Solo)

1. When I sur-vey the won-drous Cross, on which the Prince of glo-ry

died, my rich-est gain I count but loss, and pour con-tempt on all my pride.

Sopranos and Altos

2. For-bid it, Lord, that I should boast, save in the death of Christ, my

God; all the vain things that charm me most, I sac-ri-fice them to his blood.

3. See from his head, his hands, his feet, sor-row and

mf (for rehearsal only)

love flow min - gled down; did e'er such love and sor - row

meet, or thorns com - pose so rich a crown?

Tenors and Basses

4. His dy - ing crim - son like a robe, spreads o'er his bo - dy on the

tree; then I am dead to all the globe, and all the globe is dead to me.

5. Were the whole realm of na - ture mine, that were a —— ——ving pre — sent far too small; love so a - maz - ing, so di - vine, de - mands my soul, my life, my all.

Text: Isaac Watts (1674-1748)

Sit
Prayer.

Stand.

10 CROWN HIM WITH MANY CROWNS

v1 Unison

1. Crown him with many crowns, the Lamb upon his throne; hark, how the heav'n-ly an-them drowns all mu-sic but its own: a-wake, my soul, and sing of him who died for thee, and hail him as thy match-less King through all e-ter-ni-ty.

Harmony
2. Crown him the Virgin's Son,
   the God incarnate born,
   whose arm those crimson trophies won
   which now his brow adorn;
   fruit of the mystic Rose,
   as of that Rose the Stem,
   the Root, whence mercy ever flows,
   the Babe of Bethlehem.

Low voices
3. Crown him the Lord of love;
   behold his hands and side,
   rich wounds, yet visible above,
   in beauty glorified:
   High voices
   no angel in the sky
   can fully bear that sight,
   but downward bends each burning eye
   at mysteries so bright.

Harmony
4. Crown him the Lord of peace,
   whose pow'r a sceptre sways
   from pole to pole, that wars may cease,
   absorbed in prayer and praise:
   his reign shall know no end,
   and round his piercèd feet
   fair flow'rs of paradise extend
   their fragrance ever sweet.

Descant
5. Crown him the Lord of years, the Po-ten-tate of time, Cre-
All other voices

a-tor of the rol-ling spheres, in-ef-fa-bly sub-lime.

Melody: 'Diademata' by George Job Elvey (1816-1893)
Text: Matthew Bridges (1800-1894)